Panto Seas

Since the launch of The Dandy and The Beano in the late thirties, pantomime has played an important role in providing their iconic comic characters with a platform for fun and laughter. Over the Christmas period both titles staged pantomimes in differing forms. This varied collection is taken from their archives and includes pantos that ran for many pages and featured the complete cast of Beano or Dandy characters, to quick strip panto cameos. Hopefully there is something for everyone.

Oh, no, there isn't!
Oh, yes, there is!

You're in trouble when the Bash Street Kids don't like your act.

Early panto, Korky the Cat, Dandy 1938.

Don't let the Bash Street Kids organise the show.

Dick Whittington and his cat drawn by legendary artist Dudley Watkins.

Cinderella and the Ugly Sisters had their own strip in a wartime Beano.

Minnie the Minx speeds up the panto horse. Beano 1962.

No one would want to go to the Bash Street Ball.

The Pinocchio effect, Dandy Book 1957.

Desperate Dan takes one on the chin in the Cactusville panto.

THE BASH STREET KIDS
NATIVITY PLAY

CHRISTMAS IS COMING TO BEANOTOWN AND EVERYONE IS LOOKING FORWARD TO IT...

Writer and artist of this Beano extravaganza was Mike Pearse. We thought you would like to see some of the terrific illustrated script Mike first sent to Beano editor Euan Kerr, along with some of the pages as they actually appeared.

FOR INSTANCE, WALTER THE SOPTY...

MERRY CHRISTMAS, READERS!

SKIP! SKIP!

...AND DENNIS THE MENACE!

SLAP! SPLOT! SPLAT!

MERRY CHRISTMAS, WALTER!

IT WAS A DARK AND FROSTY NIGHT AND ON A LONELY HILLSIDE TWO SHEPHERDS WERE WATCHING THEIR SHEEP...

WOOF! WOOF! WOOF!

SMIFFY..! WHAT WAS THAT?!?

PERHAPS IT WAS A SHEEP THAT DOES IMPRESSIONS.

SINCE WHEN DID SHEEP GO "WOOF"?!

WELL, THAT'S WHAT SIDNEY TOLD ME!

OH REALLY..?!

MY, LOOK AT THE CRAFTSMANSHIP OF THESE FLOOR-BOARDS!

SO...TRYING TO RUIN MY NATIVITY PLAY, EH?!

PARDON ME, INNKEEPER, BUT IS THERE ANY ROOM AT THE INN?

DANNY, I'VE ALREADY TOLD YOU...!

HEY, WHEN'S IT OUR TURN?

YEAH! I'M GETTING BORED!

GET LOST! I HAVEN'T DONE MY BIT YET!

YOU CAN'T SAY "GET LOST" TO A KING!

WELL, I'M AN ANGEL, SO I OUTRANK YOU...!

BUT THERE'S THREE OF US!

SO WHAT?!

YEAH..!

I THOUGHT WE WERE ON FIRST?!

HUH! IN YOUR DREAMS...

WOOF! WOOF! WOOF!

SHUT UP..!

FIVE MINUTES LATER...

TAP! TAP! TAP!

GO AWAY...!

IT WAS A BUSY WEEK FOR TEACHER AND THE KIDS.

A WEEK OF REHEARSALS...

A WEEK OF COSTUME FITTING...

...AND MORE REHEARSALS...

...AND PROP MAKING...

...AND SCENERY PAINTING...

...AND EVEN MORE REHEARSALS...

...BUT EVENTUALLY IT HAD TO COME...

...THE NIGHT OF THE PLAY!

ER ... ONCE UPON A TIME, LONG LONG AGO...

...JOSEPH AND MARY WERE MAKING THEIR WAY TO BETHLEHEM...

INN

WHAT IS MARY RIDING?!

DUNNO! I'VE NEVER SEEN ONE OF *THOSE* BEFORE!

I HAVE... ...IN A HORROR MOVIE!

MARY, WOULD YOU LIKE TO CLIMB OFF YOUR DONKEY AND REST AWHILE?

THAT'S A DONKEY?!

IT LOOKS MORE LIKE A STEGO—

SHUSH!

YES, I AM A LITTLE TIRED FOR I AM CARRYING THE BABY JESUS IN MY TUMMY!

THEN LET ME ASK THAT INNKEEPER IF HE HAS A PLACE FOR US TO SPEND THE NIGHT.

PAF!

I'M DREADING THIS BIT...

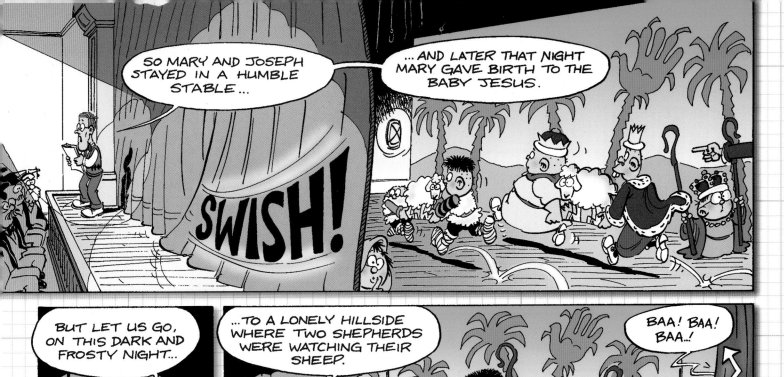

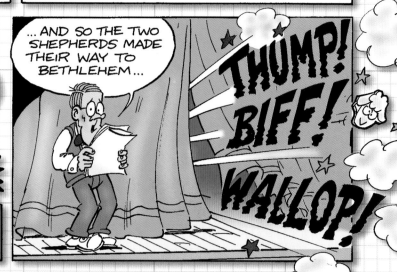

LET US NOW RETURN TO THAT HUMBLE STABLE IN BETHLEHEM...

...WHERE MARY IS PLACING THE BABY JESUS IN A MANGER.

INN STAYBUL

ACTUALLY, I'VE CHANGED MY MIND ABOUT THAT!

REALLY.

QUIET SOBS...

I'M GOING TO HOLD MY BABY JUST IN CASE HIS HEAD FALLS—

OUCH!

THUMP!

UM ... I MEAN, JUST IN CASE HE GETS STRAW UP HIS NOSE!

MA-MA!

BOO HOO HOO ..!

FIRST, THE SHEPHERDS ARRIVED TO WELCOME THE BABY JESUS.

MA-MA!

ER...QUIET DEAR!

...AND THEN CAME THE THREE KINGS BEARING GIFTS.

GASP!

I SEE THAT MATHS IS NOT ONE OF YOUR SCHOOL'S STRONG POINTS!

WAAAH!

WHERE'S 'ERBERT ?!?

I'LL LOOK FOR HIM !

BRASSNECK

YIPPEE! THIS IS GREAT FUN!

RIDE 'EM, COWBOY! THAT'S THE WAY, BRASSNECK!

WHAT A LAUGH!

IT'S not every boy who has a pal made of tin. But Charley Brand has just that — a walking, talking, metal marvel with innards full of electrical works — and his name is Brassneck

Brassneck can do everything any ordinary schoolboy can do, and lots more besides. He is always eager to join in all the horseplay — and you can see one of his pranks here, when he took part in the rehearsals for the school pantomime.

But read on to see how that pantomime began.

It was nearing Christmas when the Headmaster came along to Charley Brand's classroom to make an announcement.

ANY BOY WHO WANTS TO HELP WITH THE SCHOOL PANTOMIME CAN COME ALONG TO THE HALL AS SOON AS HE HAS FINISHED THE EXERCISE HE IS DOING!

COUNT ME IN!

But as soon as the head departed, teacher Fatso Snodgrass showed that he was all against the idea.

PANTOMIMES! BAH! HUMBUG! A WASTE OF VALUABLE TIME! YOU'LL ALL DO ANOTHER FIFTY SUMS BEFORE YOU SET FOOT OUT OF THIS CLASS-ROOM!

Having given the boys this mammoth task, Fatso left the room. This gave Brassneck a chance to climb in at the window and offer his assistance.

PERHAPS I CAN HELP, CHARLEY?

Charley made a quick adjustment to the works under a flap at the back of his metal pal's nut.

SET MY BRAINBOX TO FULL SPEED, CHARLEY!

The boys fed the problems in under the flap, and the answers came streaming out of the metal marvel's mouth!

BRASSNECK IS FANTASTIC! HE'S QUICKER THAN THE FASTEST COMPUTER!

I'VE CHECKED SOME OF THE ANSWERS. EVERY ONE IS CORRECT!

Within fifteen minutes all the sums had been completed.

BET FATSO NEVER BARGAINED FOR THIS!

And Fatso hadn't bargained for a bash on the chops either. That's what he got when the bots charged out of the classroom.

OKAY, LADS! LET'S SEE HOW THE PANTOMIME IS DOING!

Charley and his pals made a beeline for the school hall.

WHAT CAN WE DO TO HELP, SIR?

YOU CAN HELP PAINT THE SCENERY!

Unseen by the boys, Fatso came tiptoeing in pursuit.

THESE BOYS ARE NOT GOING TO GET THE BETTER OF ME!

The crafty teacher had a wicked plan in mind.

IF A MESS IS MADE WITH THE PAINT, THE HEAD WILL BE ANGRY, AND THE BOYS WILL BE SENT BACK TO THEIR CLASS-ROOM!

Fatso sneaked off with several tins of paint — unaware that Brassneck was watching him from halfway up the wall.

I'LL MAKE THESE BOYS WISH THEY'D NEVER SET FOOT IN THIS HALL!

Hurrying over to the stage control board, Brassneck pulled a lever

A trapdoor fell open beneath Fatso in the stage, and he went hurtling through it — paint pots and all.

HELP!

Fatso landed with a thump in the cellar below. He was black and blue. And he saw red.

AARGH!

What a sorry sight Fatso looked as he clambered back up on to the stage!

WHAT ARE YOU LOT LAUGHING AT?

OH, DEAR! IT LOOKS AS IF MR SNODGRASS HAS HAD AN ACCIDENT!

HO-HO!

Then as he hurried off to clean up, Fatso came upon a hamper of pantomime costumes. That gave him another brainwave.

MAYBE IF THESE COSTUMES DISAPPEARED, THE BOYS WOULD GET THE BLAME AND THEY WOULD HAVE TO RETURN TO THEIR CLASSROOM!

COSTUMES

But Brassneck had followed the mishchief maker. And the metal boy was flabbergasted to think what Fatso might do with the hamper.

I'LL DUMP THIS HAMPER IN A FURNACE!

COSTUMES

Brassneck kept right behind the nasty teacher, and his eyes popped when Fatso ended up in the Town Council rubbish yard, where there was a furnace.

BETTER STOKE UP THE FIRE FIRST!

FURNACE

COSTUM

Pressing one of his tummy switches, Brassneck set his suction-soled feet into action and walked straight up a wall. And he carried a dustbin full of rubbish with him.

HOPE I'M IN TIME TO STOP MR SNODGRASS!

Fatso was just about to throw the hamper into the furnace, when the garbage showered down on top of him.

YULK!

COSTUMES

Fatso was in a foul state. Lots of the rubbish had stuck to the wet paint on his clothes.

SNIFF! WHAT A PONG! IT'S WORSE THAN A THOUSAND SKUNKS!

The smell was so awful that Fatso had to strip off and burn his suit! Fortunately the hamper was full of clothing — though it was all very fancy.

HOPE NO ONE RECOGNISES ME IN THIS OUTFIT!

COSTUMES

As Fatso headed back to school, passers-by got a real hoot.

I'LL JUST IGNORE THAT FELLOW! HE'S OBVIOUSLY A NUT CASE!

ISN'T THAT MR SNODGRASS, THE TEACHER? TEE-HEE!

HOWDY, COWBOY! LOST YOUR HORSE? HAW-HAW!

BUS STOP

IS HE A BADDY, MA? ARE THOSE GUNS REAL?

The Headmaster saw Fatso coming and was pleased to see him.

AH! THERE YOU ARE, MR SNODGRASS, AND ENTERING INTO THE SPIRIT OF THINGS, TOO, I SEE!

WELL, ER, YOU SEE, IT'S LIKE THIS—

But the Head stopped him —and then staggered him with a new suggestion.

TELL YOU WHAT, MR SNODGRASS! THE PANTO SKIN IS MUCH TOO BIG FOR ANY OF THE BOYS. HOW ABOUT YOU AND I CLIMBING INTO IT AND TRYING IT OUT?

WHAT!

With the Head and Fatso inside the skin, Brassneck took a running jump on to the horse's back.

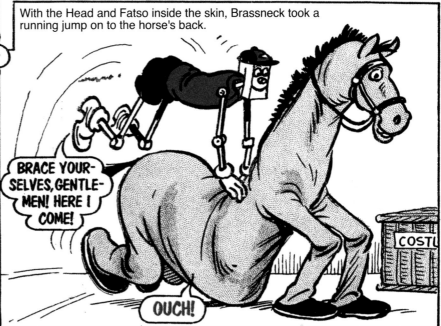

BRACE YOUR-SELVES, GENTLE-MEN! HERE I COME!

OUCH!

This was just what the Headmaster wanted, some funny antics for the horse to play. He was well pleased, for Fatso's clumsiness made the rear end of the horse do fantastic tricks.

HO-HO! I WOULDN'T LIKE TO BE IN FATSO'S SHOES!

HELP! MY HEAD IS LIKE A SPINNING TOP!

On the night of the show the panto horse was the star turn. It brought the house down with it's antics. Brassneck was on the horse's back again, only this time he was wearing sharp spurs which he dug into Fatso's rear to make him twist and turn and kick and cavort better than any panto horse ever done before. Served him right for trying to spoil the show!

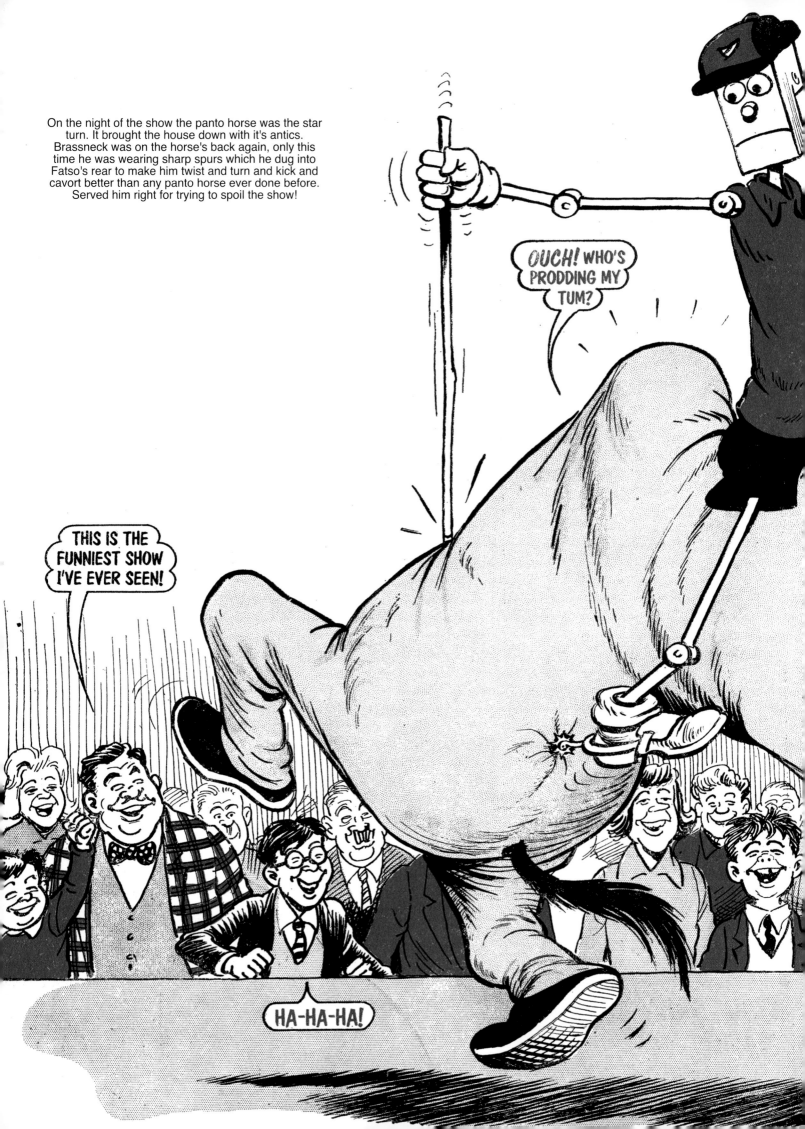

How the audience howled when Fatso missed his footing and fell from the stage.

STEADY! WATCH YOU DON'T TRAMP ON THE AUDIENCE!

HAW-HAW!

HURRAH!

ENCORE!

At the end, the Head and Fatso received a rapturous ovation. And it was amazing what it did for Fatso. It made him beam with pleasure and puff out his chest — and made him forget all he had gone through to earn such a terrific storm of cheers!

There was a big party after the show was over. Everyone had a great time — even Fatso, who was still basking in the glory of being one of the stars.

HERE'S A TOAST TO EVERYONE WHO MADE THE SCHOOL PANTO-MIME SUCH A SUCCESS!

YIPPEE! WHAT A SUPER TUCK-IN!

EAT UP, MR SNODGRASS!

STRANGE HILL SCHOOL

WHAT PANTOMIME WILL WE DO THIS YEAR?

HOW ABOUT CINDERELLA?

I COULD BE CINDERELLA AND THESE TWO COULD BE THE UGLY SISTERS.

NO! THEY'RE TOO HANDSOME!

HOW ABOUT LITTLE RED RIDING HOOD?

I COULD BE THE BIG BAD WOLF.

NO! YOU'RE NOT FRIGHTENING ENOUGH.

SNARL

WHAT ABOUT PETER PAN, SIR?

THAT'S IT! WE'LL HAVE A REHEARSAL!

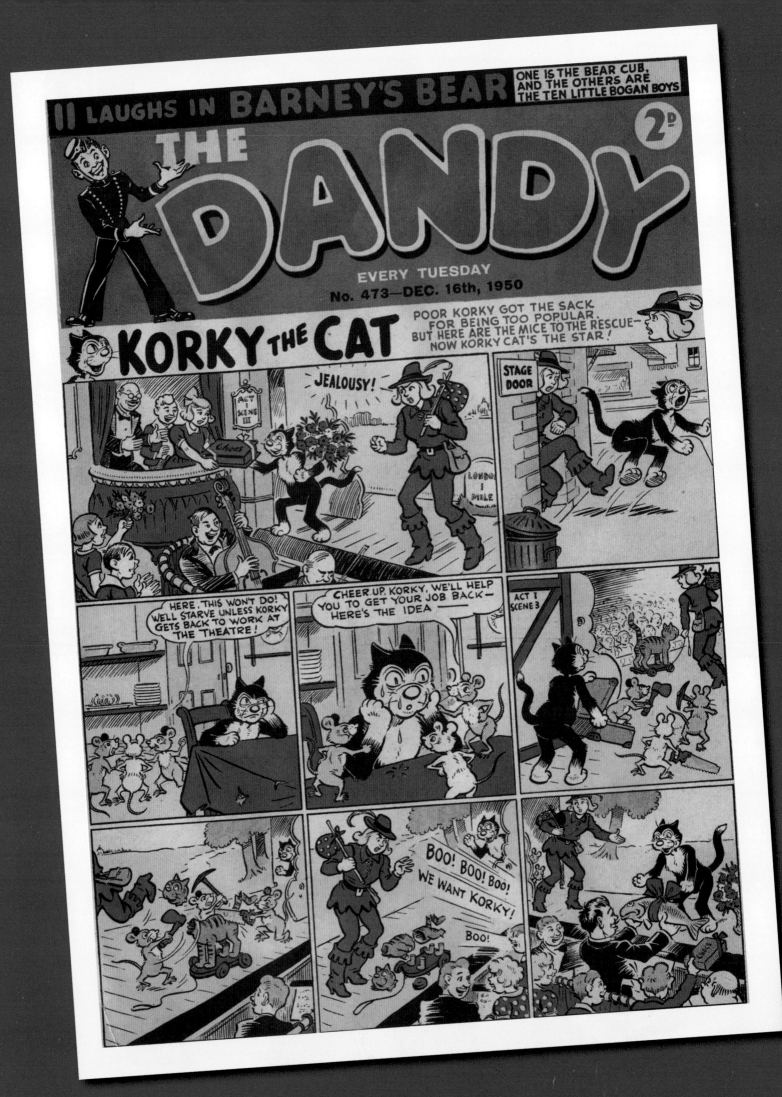

BIFFO HAS A HECTIC TIME PLAYING IN A PANTOMIME ‖ OUR PAL'S IN TROUBLE TRYING TO ACT HE'S FUNNY ONLY WHEN HE'S SACKED!

THE BEANO COMIC 2ᴅ

No 350. DECEMBER 11th 1948.

DAN 16.1.99

WATCH THIS.

PRANG! STAB! JAB! HOWL!

WE USE OUR IKKLE PALS TO BEAT ALLA BADDIES.

GO AWAY!

YEESH!

WHAM! POP! BOOT!

BRADLEY! SO YOU'RE THE PERISHER WHO'S BEEN STICKING UP THESE POSTERS!

NEXT? ANY MORE NAUGHTY SOLDIERS NEEDING DUFFED UP?

IN THAT CASE, I'M OFF TO FINE AUNT AGGIE.

DAN 16.1.99

CUT IT OUT — AN' TELL ME WHERE AUNT AGGIE IS.

A load of snivelling directions later —

AHA! FOUND HER!

ROBIN!

YOU'RE TO LATE, WEEVIL. SOON WE'LL BE MARRIED AN' I'LL BE YER UNCLE FAGIN!

Panto Lines

Why is it useless telling shopkeepers to be quiet?

Because they don't shut up till the end of the day.

King: You shall die, but you may choose to die any way you wish.

Tom: Then I choose to die of old age.

Gamekeeper: Don't you know you are not allowed to fish here?

Boy: I'm not fishing. I'm teaching this worm to swim.

Why do witches fly on brooms?

Because they love to sweep across the sky.

Spotty: The Beanotown weather forecaster had to leave town last summer.

Erbert: Why?

Spotty: The weather didn't agree with him.

Why are you running?
There's a lion loose.
Which way did it go?
Do you think I'm following it?

Mother: What? You've been fighting with Jack? I thought he was a good boy, he has such a nice face.

Jill: Well he hasn't anymore.

Teacher; Dennis, what do we call a person who is very talkative yet uninteresting?

Dennis: A teacher.

Dick: I'm thinking of going to London. What will it cost me?

Coachman: Nothing

Dick: What do you mean, Sir?

Coachman: It doesn't cost anything to think.

Jack: When people's teeth hurt they have them filled, don't they?

Mother: Yes.

Jack: My stomach aches, could I go to the sweet shop and have it filled?

Cinderberyl

AND THE Magic Button

The rotten old Editor's asked me to write a story. As usual he sez he's to poot it into proper English – as if I didn't write proper English! So here's a story – a farey tail......

CINDERBERYL wasn't feeling at all pleased. In fact, she felt just about as happy as an elephant with toothache.

Cinderberyl lived in a tumbledown old cottage with her three ugly brothers – Pete, Tweet and Skeet. Apart from going to school, she had to do all the cooking and cleaning for those three horrors.

But on her afternoon off, Cinders (we'll call her that for short) used to go off to the park for a game of football. What a player she was! She could run rings round all the Gasworks gang and the other lads who played there.

In fact, she could play so well that Pete, Tweet and Skeet became jealous of her. And they told her – last week it was – that she'd have to stop because she was kicking her shoes to pieces. What's more, they hid the shoes, just to stop her from sneaking off to play football. As if she'd do anything she wasn't supposed to do.

At the moment, Cinders was frantically searching every place she could think of, looking for her shoes. If she found them, she might just possibly take a stroll to the park. And if a football happened to be kicked in her direction – well, she'd jolly well kick it back. And nuts to Pete, Tweet and Skeet.

– for Beryl was the author of it!

But no matter where she looked, Cinders couldn't find her shoes. She found a piece of an old jigsaw, a broken trumpet, and three squashed, mouldy toffees, but you couldn't play football wearing any of THOSE, could you?

Sucking one of the mouldy toffees, she sat brooding. It was then that she noticed something glistening on the floor behind the sideboard.

"Hmm! Must have fallen from one of the sideboard drawers when I was rummaging," she thought.

She crawled below the sideboard, and picked up a shiny button.

"Looks like a button off an old army uniform," she muttered, giving it a rub. "Fat lot of good THAT is. Wish it was a pair of football boots!"

Suddenly a bright light flashed before her eyes. Cinders blinked – and when she opened her eyes again, there, standing before her, was a tall lady in a long dress, holding a sort of stick in one hand.

"Wh-wh-what-er-who are YOU?" stammered Cinderberyl.

"I am your fairy godmother. I came directly you rubbed the magic button," replied the lady.

"Crumbs! Crikey! And gosh!" gulped Cinders. "Not to mention golly!"

"I heard you wishing that the magic button was a pair of football boots," continued the fairy godmother. "Your wish will be granted – with one wave of my magic wand."

So saying she raised her little stick. In the twinkling of an eye, Cinders found that the button she'd been holding had magically changed into the most super-duper pair of football boots!

"Why, that's just great!" whooped Cinders. "They're my size, too."

"Of course," smiled the fairy godmother.

"Now I can go and play football in the park," whooped Cinders. "Oh – thanks a bundle!"

"Wait! There's just one thing," said the fairy godmother quickly. "I know you'd have trouble from your ugly brothers if you got home late. So don't wear the boots one second after the stroke of five o'clock, or something unpleasant will happen."

Cinders, hurriedly lacing up the boots, was hardly listening.

"Oh-er-yes. All right," she agreed excitedly. "I'm off, now. Thanks again!"

"I'm off, too," replied the fairy godmother, as Cinders darted out of the door. "Have a good game." Then in another flash of light, the fairy godmother disappeared almost as quickly as Cinders had done..

GOALS GALORE

WHEN Cinderberyl reached the park, a game of football was in full swing. The Gasworks gang were playing against Ginger Johnson's Eleven. Well – it was really Ginger Johnson's Ten, for Weepy Wilson had gone home crying when the ball hit him on the nose. The score was 18-1 for the Gasworks gang.

Cinderberyl, in her shining new boots, was soon to change all that.

"I'll play centre-forward, Ginger," she called.

Thundering on to the field, she intercepted the ball and went dribbling up the field. Beating six men, thanks to some clever footwork – and a few sharp digs with her elbows, but there wasn't a referee, so it didn't matter – she slammed in a shot. What a shot it was. It took the Gasworks goalie in the tummy, lifted him right off his feet, and carried him bodily between the goal-post jackets.

That made the score 18-2.

Soon it was 18-3. Then 18-4. And 18-8 and 18-14. At one minute to five o'clock the score was 18-18. Mind you, Cinders hadn't scored all the goals – only 16 of them.

She was on the ball again, bearing down on the Gasworks goal, when the clock in the nearby church steeple began to strike five o'clock.

Needless to say, Cinders had forgotten all about the fairy godmother's warning. One-two-three-four-five chimed the clock. On the fifth stoke, Cinder's right foot was swinging back to belt the ball. It lashed forward.

5 o'clock – time for a shock!

Next instant – whoosh! – the boot flew off her foot and rocketed through the air. Worse than that – it didn't stop till it cracked against the head of a little fat man strolling across the park not far away.

"Oh, crumbs!" breathed Cinders.

"Oogh! Ow!" moaned the little man, and whirled round in time to see Cinderberyl galloping off, with a bootless foot and a turn of speed that many a racehorse would have envied.

The Gasworks gang and Ginger Johnson's Ten departed, too, squabbling amongst themselves as they ran, about who would have won the match if Cinders' boot hadn't upset things. Meanwhile the little man picked up the boot that had struck him.

"Hmm!" he muttered, turning it over and over and examining it ever so carefully for some time. "A very small size. And it was a girl wearing it. Shouldn't be too difficult to trace her."

If Cinderberyl, who was arriving breathlessly at the tumbledown cottage, had heard these words, she would have quaked. But she didn't, of course. (Well, it's about half a mile from the park to the cottage!)

"Too bad I lost that super boot," she muttered to herself. "Never mind – at least I've got home ahead of Pete, Tweet and Skeet. I'll get on with making the tea, and they won't even know I've been out..."

BOPO THE CLOWN

NEXT day, Cinders was sleepy in school, what with all the housework and everything – not to mention the fact that she'd been up till after ten at night, so that she could sneak out to the park to look for her lost football boot after the ugly brothers were asleep. But, alas, she hadn't found it.

"That little fat man must have pinched it, or taken it to the police, or something," she thought gloomily, and fell into an uneasy doze. The sound of the bell ringing woke her. It was the signal for the end of the period, and Cinders' class had to go along to another room.

Marching along the corridor, Cinders happened to glance into a room where a class had already assembled. She froze in horror. Standing with the teacher was the little fat man and he was holding Cinders' lost football boot!

"Mr Simpson wants to find the girl who owns this boot," Cinders heard the teacher saying. "He thinks the person to whom it belongs may be afraid to own up – so I want every one of you to try it on. It's a very unusual size."

Cinders gulped, and hurried on down the corridor, all of a tremble.

"Got to do something before they come to OUR class with that boot," she muttered.

But she didn't know WHAT she could do – until her teacher, Miss King, left the class unattended for a few minutes while she went to see the headmaster.

Quick as a flash, Cinders jumped up from her desk.

"Er – got an errand to do," she told her classmates briefly. "I'll be back before Miss King is – I hope!"

With that, she hopped out of the window. She fled across the playground, and raced at top speed down the street. Her destination was a circus, which had come to town a couple of days before.

"Hope old Bopo the clown's still with this lot," she panted, as she ran into the circus ground close to the school playing-field.

Her luck was in. She bumped into Bopo just as the clown was stepping out of his caravan.

"Hello! Remember me?" cried Cinders. "I met you last year when you lost your false nose and I found it!"

"Why, yes I do!" beamed Bopo. "Pleased to see you

Oh dear, oh dear, oh dear! – There's trouble brewing here!

again. I still have the same nose."

"I knows – ha! ha!" replied Cinders, trying to look cheerful. "But, look – I'm in a big hurry. There's a little favour I'd like you to do for me."

"Anything I can," chuckled Bopo. "You name it…"

DEFEAT FOR CINDERS

CINDERS arrived breathlessly back through the classroom window in the nick of time. Under her arm she carried a big parcel.

She had just plumped herself down behind her desk when the classroom door opened. In strode Miss King, accompanied by the little fat man with the boot!

"Pay attention, class," said Miss King. "This is Mr Simpson, and he has come to the school to find the owner of this unusual football boot. He already knows that the owner is a girl. If she is here, will she please stand up?"

"Hmm! I'm not really the owner, "thought Cinders." It belongs to my fairy godmother, I suppose! So I'll sit tight!"

So Cinders slumped even lower at her desk.

"Nobody?" said Miss King. "Very well – you will come up here, one by one as I call out your names, and try on the boot. It's a very unusual size. If the owner is here, we'll soon find her."

"Not if I can help it," muttered Cinders to herself.

Miss King began to call out the names from the class register.

"Amelia Bates…"

A small, red-headed girl came out to the classroom floor, removed her shoe and tried to thrust her foot into the boot. Not a hope – her foot was about three sizes too big.

"Sandra Dobson," went on Miss King.

Sandra couldn't even get her toes into the boot.

"Eileen Johnson… Jane Morgan… Mandy Platt…" One by one the girls came out. None of them could wear the boot.

"Cinderberyl Samson…"

CLUMP…CLUMP…CLUMP…CLUMP…CLUMP…

The class simply goggled as Cinders slogged out from her desk, wearing a pair of special clown's boots about three foot long! They were Bopo's, of course, but Cinders hoped that Miss King and Mr Simpson wouldn't know that!

"What on earth is this nonsense, Cinderberyl?" thundered Miss King.

"N-nonsense?" answered Cinderberyl, trying to look innocent. "What do you mean, Miss King? Oh, you mean me having to try on that football boot when I've got such huge feet? Yes, indeed! You can see for yourself, Mr Simpson, sir, my feet would never fit that football boot."

Miss King spluttered with rage.

"Take off these ridiculous boots at once, girl," she snorted. "We all know you don't have feet that size."

"You do? Oh dear!" replied Cinders gloomily, and slowly pulled off the big boots.

"Now – try on the football boot," commanded Miss King.

Unwillingly, Cinders slid her foot into the football boot, trying to spread her toes to stop the foot going in. No good – the boot fitted, and all Cinders' tricks couldn't alter the fact. Mr Simpson was delighted.

"So, YOU'RE the girl who was playing football in the park yesterday," he cried. "You hit me on the head when your boot flew off – remember?"

"Um-er-now that you mention it," muttered Cinders, "I did-er-kick off a boot yesterday. Um-er-this MIGHT be it here."

There was a crafty plan afoot – and Bopo the clown was only too willing to help!

To Cinders' dismay – big feet don't pay!

"No 'mights' about it, girl!" bellowed Miss King. "You're the culprit all right. Shall I punish her, Mr Simpson, or –"

"Oh, no!" The little fat man shook his head vigorously. "I don't want her punished. All I want is to know the name of the shop where she bought her boots. I'm the local football club's manager, and I've never seen a finer football boot than this one. I MUST have a set for my team, and therefore I have to know where this boot came from."

Cinders perked up.

"If that's all you want to know, sir, that's easy," she declared. "I got it from my fairy godmother!"

Miss King almost choked.

"CINDERBERYL! YOU IMPUDENT GIRL!" she shouted. Then, with an effort, she controlled her anger. "All right – we'll give you one more chance," she rasped. "Tell the gentleman where you REALLY got your boots."

"B-but-"

Cinders was about to repeat that they really DID come from her fairy godmother. Fortunately, she realised what trouble THAT would cause, so she didn't. Instead, she had a brainwave.

"I-er-they were a sort of present," she blurted out, "so I don't know what shop they came from. But the maker's name might be printed on the side of the other boot – the one I still have at home."

"Yes-yes-very probably," agreed Mr Simpson. "I'm sure Miss King will give you leave of absence for half an hour to take me to your home to examine the boot."

"Certainly," agreed Cinders' teacher. "But remember, Cinderberyl – straight back to school afterwards."

"Yes, Miss," muttered Cinders, slipping into her own worn shoes before marching off with the football manager.

"But if there ISN'T a name on the other boot," she thought to herself – "what'll I tell Mr Simpson then…"

HAPPY ENDING

SURE enough, Cinders' worst fears came to pass. There wasn't a marking of any kind inside the other boot. Mr Simpson scowled.

"Never mind – just tell me who gave you the boots, and I'll go and ask THEM," he said.

"Oh, crumbs!" thought Cinders, looking blankly at him. "If I say fairy godmother again, he'll go back and tell Miss King that I've been cheeky!"

She was holding the second of the boots as she spoke, trying frantically to think of some reply to make to Mr Simpson. "Wish these boots were back to being a magic button again," she muttered, half to herself.

Flash! Next instant, the boot in her hand disappeared. So did the boot that the astonished Mr Simpson had been holding. And resting in Cinders' hand was the magic button.

"Oh, boy!" whooped Cinders. With a quick rub of the button, she called out – "Fairy godmother, come quick! You're wanted!"

In another flash of light, the fairy godmother appeared. The football manager stood staring, goggle-eyed.

Cinders has the smallest feet in school – and the biggest boots, by far!

Life is simply grand – when there's help from Fairyland!

"What is your wish?" asked the fairy godmother, smiling sweetly at Cinders.

"Tell this gentleman where you got the boots that I had to get rid of to get back the button to get you here, if you know what I mean," grinned Cinders.

The fairy godmother turned to Mr Simpson. "From Fairyland, of course," she said. "Where else?"

Mr Simpson glared. He was recovering from his first surprise.

"This is some sort of trick," he roared. "Don't give me any of that nonsense about Fairyland."

It was the fairy godmother's turn to look annoyed.

"Nonsense, did you say? How dare you!" she stormed.

Seizing Cinders' broom, she advanced on Mr Simpson, swinging the broom-end like an axe.

"Help!" croaked the football manager. And he departed in a cloud of dust, closely pursued by the furious fairy godmother.

Cinderberyl sat down, beaming at the magic button.

"Well – that got rid of HIM!" she chuckled. "Now, I've just had a terrific brainwave..."

She rubbed the button again. Instantly the fairy godmother reappeared, breathing heavily.

"What-pant-is your wish?" she inquired.

"I wish you to do all the cooking and housework for me in future, and to keep my three ugly, horrible brothers in order," demanded Cinders.

"Oh, gracious!" gasped the fairy godmother. "Oh, woe is me! What a low-down wish. It shouldn't be allowed!"

But there was no way she could refuse Cinders' request. Orders were orders – especially magic ones. Gloomily the fairy godmother grabbed a broom and a dustpan and set to work.

"Those ugly brothers had better

behave, or I'll turn them into frogs, or something!" she muttered threateningly to herself.

"Hee-hee!" giggled Cinderberyl. "I can see that things are going to be different from now on. Especially for my brothers. But for ME, life's going to be just GREAT!"

And gleefully clutching the magic button, Cinders headed back to school – wearing the biggest grin in the whole wide world!

The fairy godmother had taken a sudden dislike to Mr Simpson!

I bet you lot think it wasn't troo about the Farey Godmother and everything? Well – who do you think really wrote the story? Not me! The Farey Godmother, that's who.
(But don't tell the Editor!)

20930

BEANO 25-12-93 P.24

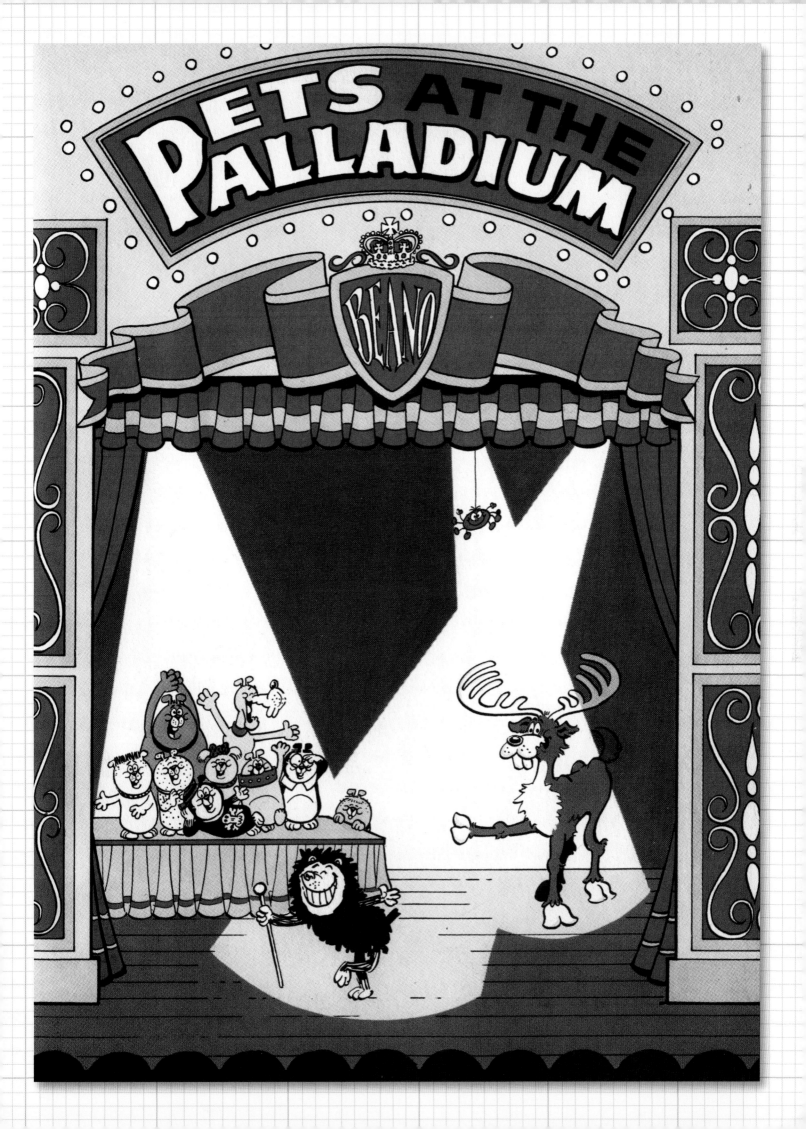

PETS at the PALLADIUM

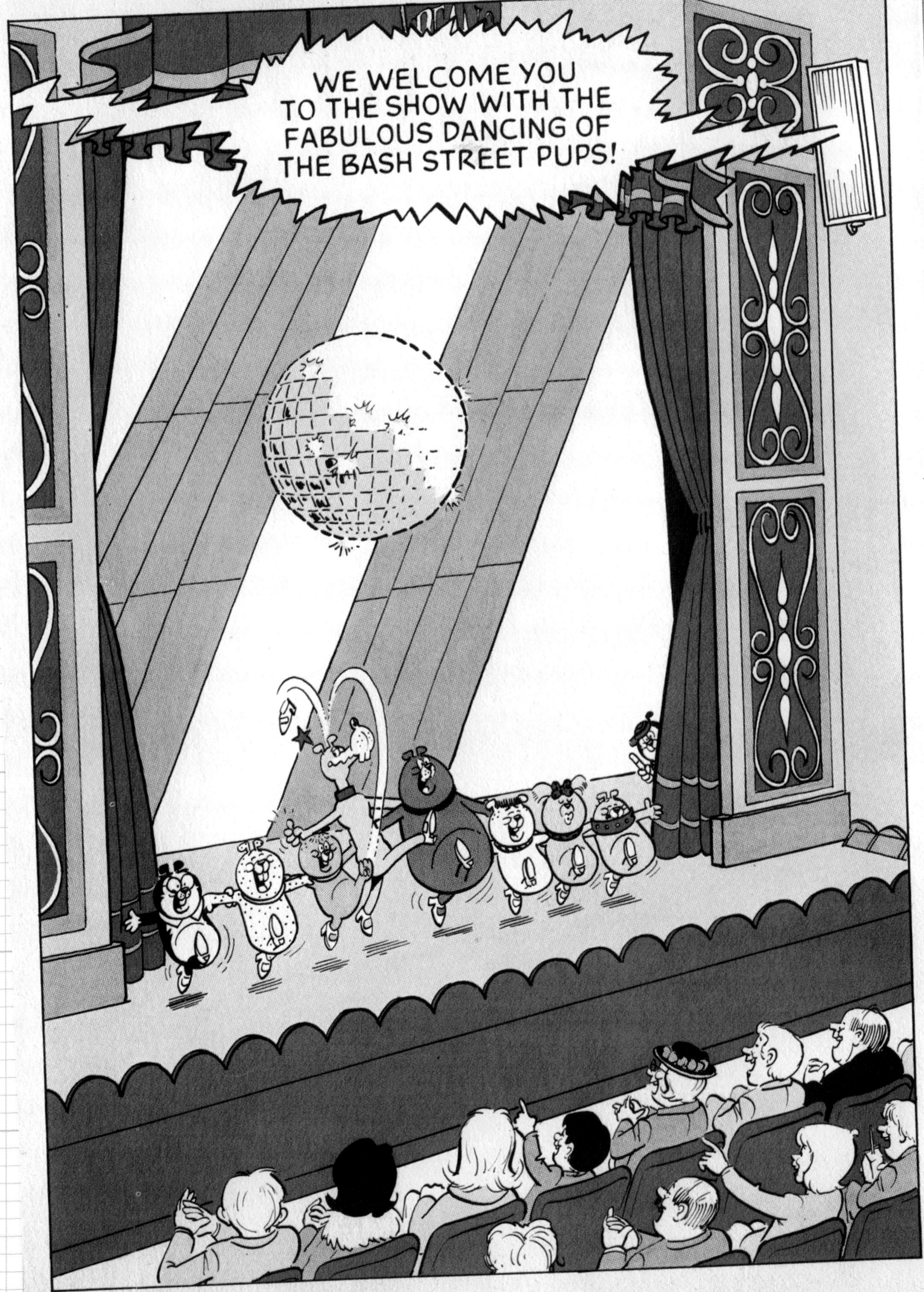

PETS at the PALLADIUM

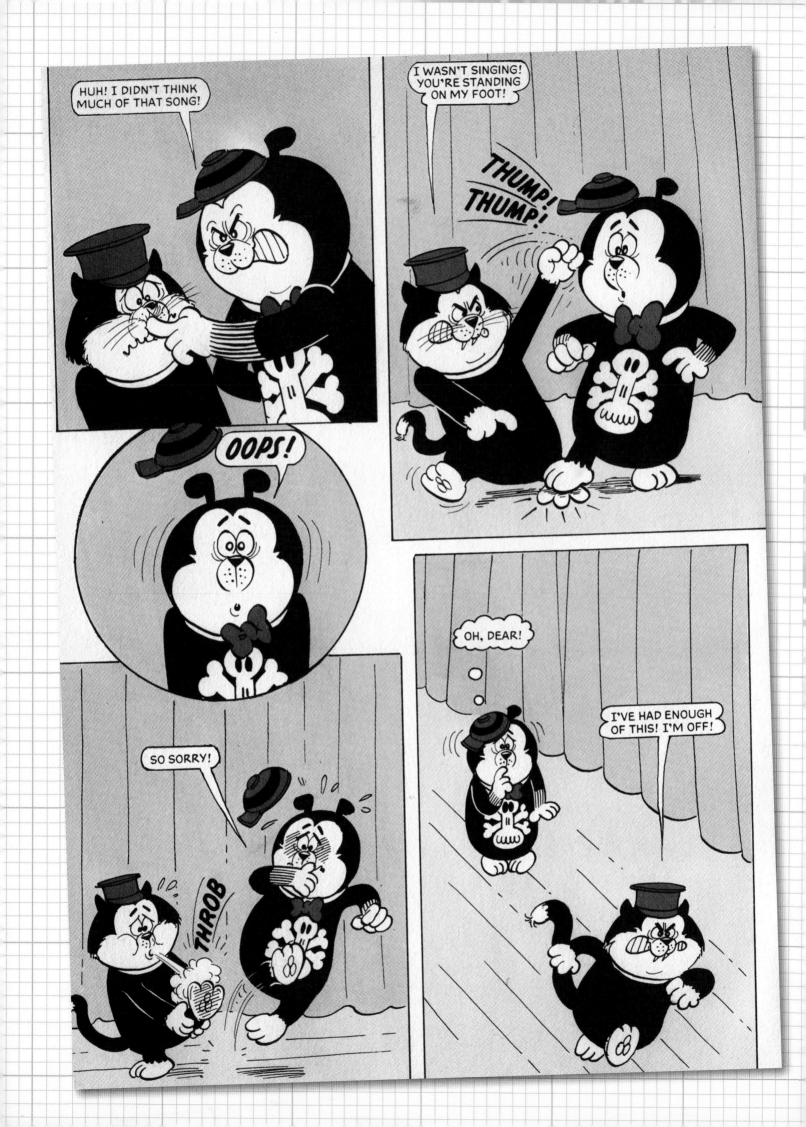

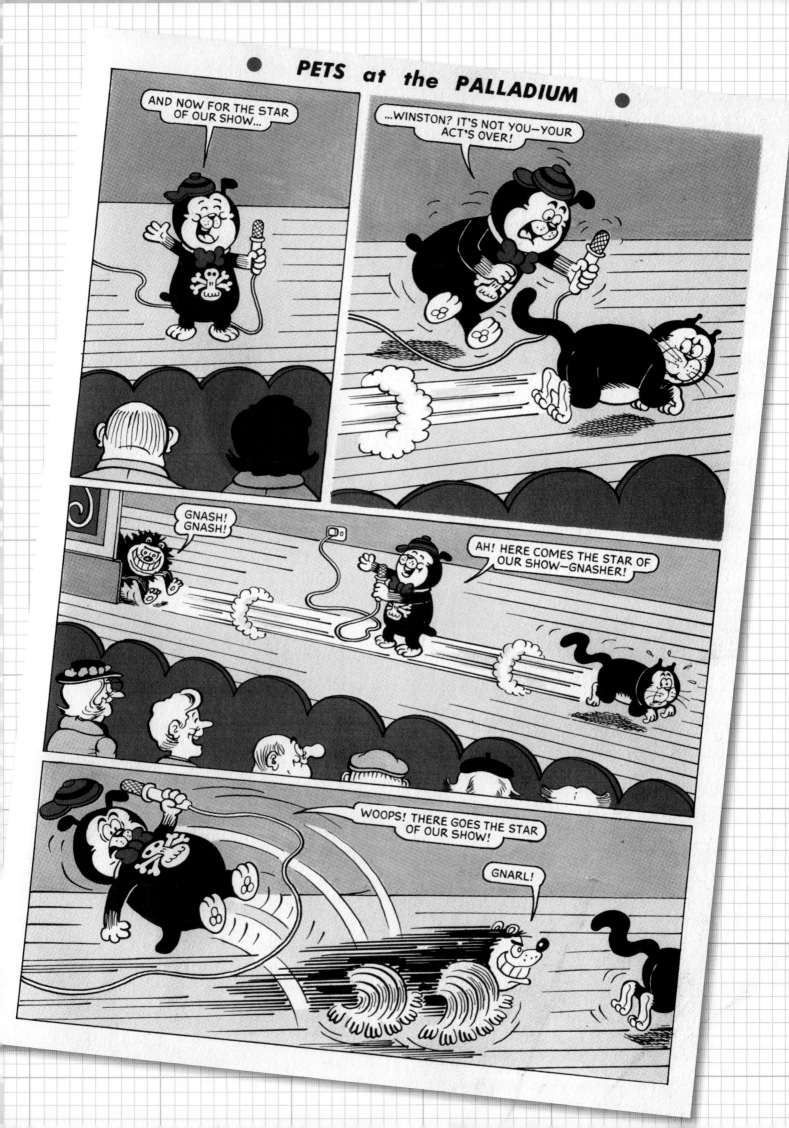

GNASHER'S NEXT IMPRESSIONS—
SEE IF YOU CAN GUESS WHAT THEY ARE!
ANSWERS AT FOOT OF PAGE.

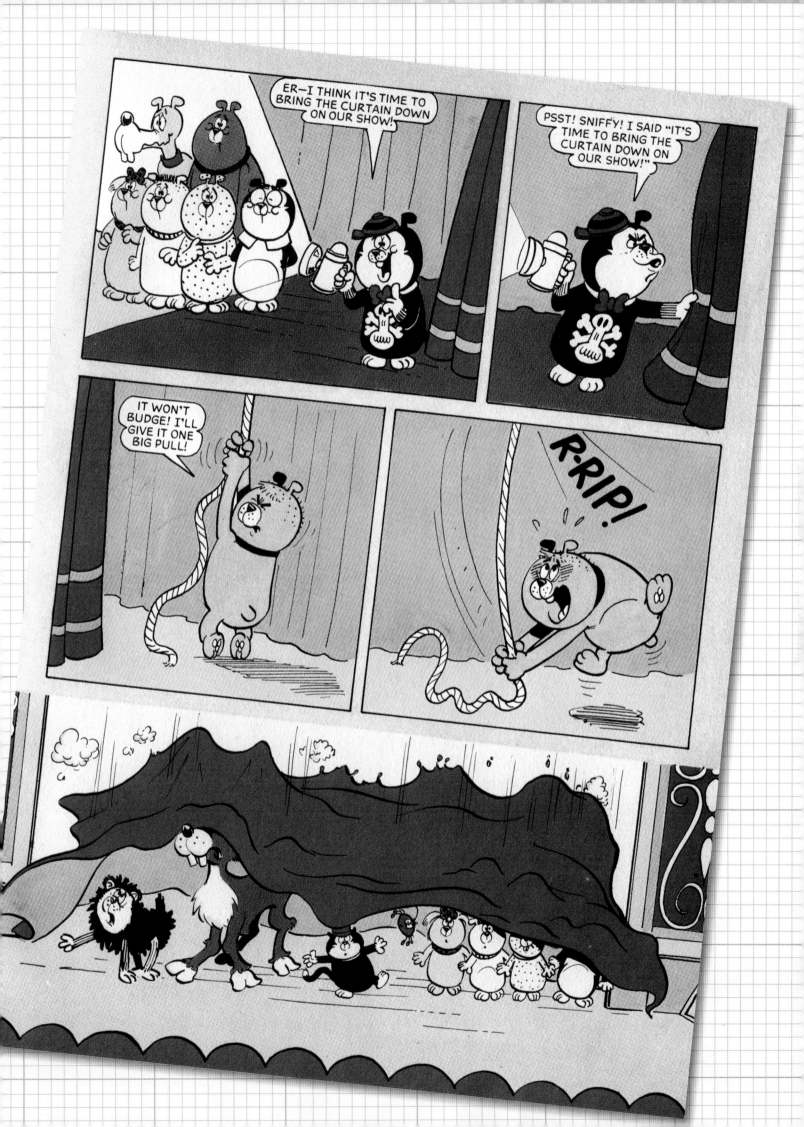

Panto Lines

Smiffy: Were you a good pupil at school, dad?

Mr Smiff: Why yes, I used to say my lessons so well that the teacher made me stay behind and repeat them to her after class.

Teacher: If you add 387, and 673, then double it and divide by 5, what would you get?

Smiffy: The wrong answer.

Lord Snooty: I want some peppah.

Store assistant: Black, white or Cayenne?

Lord Snooty: No, you fool, writing peppah!

Dad: Roger, I hear you got detention at school today. Why was that?

Roger: Teacher told us to write an essay on laziness, and I sent in a blank sheet.

King: You are sentenced to ten years in the dungeon. Do you have anything to add?

Tom: No, but I'd like to subtract.

Dad: Where are you going?

Minnie: Oh, just for a stroll.

Dad: Then stroll about the lawn, and take the mower with you.

Boy: Why is your cat wearing black boots?

Dick: the brown ones are at the cobblers.

Smiffy: What have I learned today, Teacher?

Teacher: Why, that's a funny question to ask.

Smiffy: Well, they are sure to ask me when I get home.

Danny: How do you cure a cold?

Smiffy: Drink a glass of orange juice after a hot bath.

Danny: Does it work?

Smiffy: I dunno, I haven't finished drinking the bath yet.

DANNY LONGLEGS

Danny Longlegs and his two pals, Bunty Evans and Tubby Perkins, were trying their very, very best to sneak into Bozo's Travelling Pantomime, which had arrived in the town that day. It was a simple matter for Danny to peep through the little skylight in the big tent, for, though only a schoolboy, he was ten feet tall. However, the bad-tempered manager spotted the pals.

But Danny was too interested in what he saw going on inside the tent to notice the manager. There in bed lay one of the performers, and at his side stood another, his foot swathed in bandages. On the front of the second man's tunic Danny read the words, "Panto Horse, Front Legs." The sick man acted as the Back Legs of the Panto Horse.

The manager was very furious when he knew the Panto Horse would not be able to appear. Next moment Danny lost his balance, and with a ripping of canvas he fell into the tent. The Panto performers certainly looked amazed as the ten feet tall schoolboy hurtled into their midst. They had seen many strange sights in their time, but never one like this.

But the manager's crafty brain had been working quickly, and, before Danny could get to his feet, the man had seized the lad. "You stay where you are," he bellowed. "I've got a job for you." With that he ordered the men to bring forward the parts of the horse and had Danny dressed in them.

The performance was due to start in a few minutes. Danny was led from the tent and a dwarf placed on his back. The little man carried a loud speaker and, as Danny pranced around among the crowds, the dwarf shouted to them, "Roll up, roll up, the most amazing performance ever!" The people made for the tent doors, where the rascally manager stood rubbing his hands.

On the stage Danny kept up his act with the little dwarf, while the audience laughed and cheered. Suddenly Danny's attention was attracted by a strange noise behind the canvas – the chink of money. All at once he realised someone was stealing the evening's takings. He must stop the thief, or the Panto performers would get no money for their evening's work.

Forgetting he was meant to be a horse, Danny straightened his back. He gripped the canvas with one hand and peered over. There stood the rascally manager busily filling his pouch with the money. As he caught Danny's gaze he turned towards the door where his horse stood ready saddled. The other performers did not see what was going on.

In a flash Danny had knocked over the canvas scenery. He had no intention of allowing the rascally manager to escape. But the dwarf was determined to come, too, and, as Danny leapt towards the door, he leapt also and grabbed the horse's tail. Other members of the company joined the chase, but the manager had mounted his swift horse and was off.

Out of the big tent rushed the company, with Danny at their head. Bunty and Tubby, who had been searching for Danny since the show started, now went into action with stones and catapult. It seemed, however, that the manager would escape on his fine horse, but Danny's long legs were already covering the ground at an amazing speed.

The dwarf made a special effort and managed to heave himself into the saddle on Danny's back. Danny stretched out one long arm and grabbed the manager. "You'll pay for this," the boy cried, "and for all the other mean things you did. Just wait till the others catch up on you." As Danny finished speaking the rest of the pursuers arrived on the scene.

All the manager's blustering threats and then pleas for mercy were ignored. Holding him by one leg, Danny turned him upside down and allowed the money to drop from his pouch. Some soldiers from a nearby castle had joined the crowd, and laughed as they saw the manager made prisoner. "Leave him to us," one of them cried. "We'll deal with him."

With the money retrieved from the manager the Panto folk bought loads of good things to eat. They made Danny their guest of honour, and soon he was enjoying a large meal of chicken-pie and a huge dish of fruit with cream. The only one who did not enjoy the party was the rascally manager, who at that moment was being ducked in the nearby pond.

GROAN!

ROTTERS!

WE HAVE TO EARN SPENDING-MONEY SOMEHOW!

McKENZIES BURGERS ARE BEST

EAT A McKEN

POP IN TO McKEN

And —

IT'S TIME WE TAUGHT THE JOCKS A THING OR TWO ABOUT BEARS!

Later —

ALL THIS WORK GIVES YOU A REALLY GOOD APPETITE. IT'S YOUR TURN TO MAKE THE PORRIDGE, ANGUS.

OKAY!

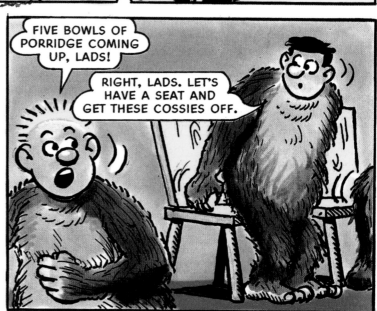

FIVE BOWLS OF PORRIDGE COMING UP, LADS!

RIGHT, LADS. LET'S HAVE A SEAT AND GET THESE COSSIES OFF.

But —

AARGH! WHO'S SAWN THROUGH THE LEG OF MY CHAIR?

AND WHO'S LEFT NETTLES ON MY CHAIR?

AND WHO'S STOLEN THE SEAT FROM MY CHAIR?

PARDING ME! MUST BE SOMETHING I ATE!

THRRPPS!

CRASH!

Whoopee cushion!

Seed feed!

"BABY-FACE"

FINLAYSON

SO—

CAN I HAVE THAT BOOK ON THE TOP SHELF?

BUT OF COURSE, SMALL SIR!

SNARL!

SQUAWK!

BONK!

W-OOF!

THIS IS THE BOOK I WAS REALLY AFTER!

NURSERY RHYMES

BUT—

WHAT A LOAD OF RUBBISH! I COULD WRITE BETTER STUFF MYSELF!

NURSERY RHYMES

IN FACT, I THINK I WILL—TURN THE PAGES TO SEE MY MAGNIFICENT EFFORTS!

The Auditions begin —

AUDITIONS

SKIP!

I'M THE DIRECTOR! GIVE ME DICTION, PRESENCE, LUVVY. PROJECT YOURSELF!

NO, BIFFO! YOU'RE TOO QUIET. NEXT!

I'M CALAMITY JAMES AND I'D LIKE A PART IN YOUR —

TOO UNLUCKY. NEXT!

PWP!

WOW!

WHIZZ!

HELLO! AND WELCOME . . . ALAS, POOR YORIC . . . BETTER TO SUFFER . . . AND ARROWS . . . A DAGGER I SEE . . . ?

And —

AW, NO! THIS DOESN'T LOOK MUCH FUN.

FAL-DA-LAH!

HOW NICE!

HOP!

SKIP!

SKIP!

PRANCE!

WISH SOMEONE WOULD LIVEN THINGS UP!

YAWN!

TWIRL!

HOP!

OUTTA MY WAY, SOFTYS!

OO! CHARMING!

OWCH! CHARMING, I'M SURE!

OUCH!

SHOVE!

PRINCE CHARMING!

THAT'S ME, MINDERELLA!

WANNA BOOGIE?

WIGGLE!

Back to the panto, Readers!

I'M BACK! GET THE TELLY ON.

CHOMP!

Soon —

WHAT A LOVELY BALL! I HAD A GREAT TIME.

ME, TOO! SMASHING!

CLOMP!

SSH!

DING-DONG!

AW WHAT NOW? I'M TRYING TO WATCH THIS.

I'LL GET IT!

YOU SEE, SHE LEFT THIS! I WANT TO FIND HER. SO I'M TRYING EVERYONE IN TOWN. TRY IT, PLEASE!

I'LL TRY IT, PRINCE CHARMING!

ME!

BEST WISHES
FROM DESPERATE DAN
AND HIS DANDY PALS!

CINDERELLA AND THE UGLY SISTERS

Pantomime inspired this strip that appeared in a wartime Beano. It was drawn by the seventeen year old artist Basil Blackaller.

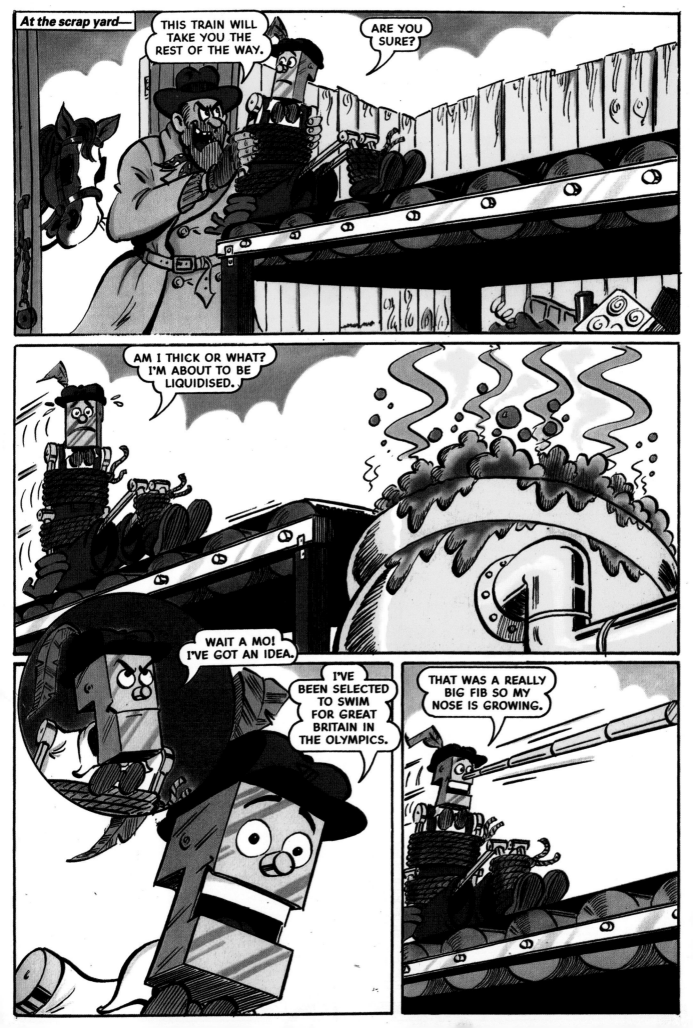

Here's a funny tale for you –

BERYL AND THE Beanstalk

The Editor asked me to write a story for this book. I told him we have two storeys on our house, and would won of THEM do, but he said, no, he wanted won that I had wrote not lived in. He insulted me, too, for he said that when I did it he would put it into proper English. Just to pleez him – and also to give me the chance to put a stink bomb in his desk when I brought it into his office – I wrote it, and here it is.

BERYL was standing outside the poor but humble home where she lived with her poor Mum and Dad. (They must be poor, she knew, because she had often heard people saying, "Poor THEM, having to live with HER.")

She wasn't standing there alone, because Mum was standing with her, so that made two of them, and they were both arguing.

"If it wasn't YOU who spread the boot polish on my sandwich, then who was it?" demanded Mum.

"Maybe it was Dad," suggested Beryl solemnly. "He always polishes the shoes, doesn't he?"

"Yes – but he doesn't polish my SANDWICHES," snapped Mum.

"Well, all I know," said Beryl, looking a bit annoyed, "is that if you hadn't refused me a sixth helping of cornflakes at breakfast time, then maybe whoever it was wouldn't have done it."

in the words of you-know-who!

"Ah! So it was you!" screeched Mum.

"Was me what?" replied Beryl suspiciously.

"Put polish on my sandwiches!" Mum roared. Beryl started towards the kitchen.

"If you say so, Mum – I'll go and do it right away," she said sweetly. "But I thought you didn't like the taste."

"Oh, you – you. Just wait till your dad gets home!" shouted Mum, shaking her fists in the air.

At that moment Dad came marching up the path, wearing the scowl that he always wore when he knew Beryl was at home.

"All right – I AM home," he growled. "What's she been up to this time?"

Beryl was in a spot – but she knew a way out.

"Er – Dad," she put in hastily, "where are the flowers you said you were going to bring for Mum?"

"Flowers? Flowers for ME, Dad?" exclaimed Mum. "How nice of you. Where are they?"

Dad looked dismayed and baffled and crafty all at the same time.

"I – er – I – er – forgot to pick them up from the flower-seller," he muttered. "Here's five shillings, Beryl. Go and fetch them." He bent low as he handed over the cash, and hissed in Beryl's ear – "I never said anything about getting flowers for Mum!"

"Well, you have now," whispered Beryl, and added in a louder voice – "Good job I reminded Dad, isn't it, Mum?"

"Yes, thank you very much Beryl," said Mum, all smiles now. "We'll say no more about the boot polish sandwiches."

"Boot polish sandwiches?" gasped Dad.

"Er – yes – it's nothing, Dad," said Mum in a soothing voice. "I like them – I really do."

Beryl gave Dad a friendly grin.

"I'll be off then," she said heartily. "If there's any change from the five bob, can I – ?"

"No – YOU CAN'T!" exploded Dad.

Beryl slouched off, muttering "Old Meanie" under her breath.

Five minutes later she reached the market square, in one corner of which an old woman flower-seller always sat. When she saw Beryl coming the old lady looked a bit alarmed.

"If you're here to play tricks," she grumbled, "then you'd just better hop it."

But Beryl didn't hop it.

"Have you any five-bob bunches selling at six-pence?" she demanded. "There's a sale on at the furniture shop an' I thought if THEY could have a sale, then maybe you – "

"Well, now, I don't exactly have a sale," cut in the old woman craftily, but with every five-bob bunch of

daffodils I give a magic bean free of charge."

"A magic bean?" gasped Beryl, her eyes lighting up. "What does THAT do?"

"It grows like magic – that's what it does," whispered the old woman mysteriously.

"Grows big, eh?" exclaimed Beryl, getting all excited. "Hmm – maybe I could plant it in the garden beside the apple tree – the one that Dad put the barbed wire

There's a mighty surprise – for the giant in the skies!

round to stop me getting at the apples. If the bean plant grows big enough, then maybe I could climb up and reach an apple. Right – a bunch of daffodils and a magic bean, please!"

"Good! Here you are," replied the old woman, reaching into her basket.

"Don't bother wrapping the magic bean!" said Beryl grandly.

When Beryl departed the old woman began to snigger softly.

"Magic bean, my eye!" she chortled to herself. "But I'm glad I had a few beans in my bag left over from the lot I bought yesterday at the greengrocer's. It helped me get a sale, that old bean did."

Meanwhile Beryl hurried home and handed over the flowers. Then she sneaked out and planted the bean alongside Dad's apple-tree.

After that she went off for a walk because it was bedtime and she could hear Mum shouting for her.

When Mum had shouted herself nearly hoarse Beryl returned and said brightly:

"What was that you were saying, Mum?"

"Croak – croak!" said Mum.

"Pardon?" said Beryl. "Did you say 'cake?' Thanks, I'll have some. I like cake for supper."

And so she did, while Mum croaked and croaked until she lost her voice altogether.

THE BIG ONE!

BERYL went to bed and slept like a log, except for the three or four times she got up to take some more cake from the larder. The last time she did this was just after dawn, and she happened to notice there didn't seem to be much daylight getting into the room. So she looked out, and what she saw gave her quite a turn, I don't mind telling you. A beanstalk a million feet high or thereabouts – that was what she saw. It stretched right up into the clouds, and they weren't low-lying clouds either. (Who ever heard of clouds lying? Even the lowest clouds don't tell lies. They can't even talk!)

Beryl jumped into her clothes and crept out of the house and began to climb.

Up she went, climbing like the Olympic champion she deserves to be, and an hour or two later she reached the topmost tip of that beanstalk.

Now, you wouldn't think there'd be any land up there, would you? Well, if that's what you wouldn't think you'd be dead wrong. For there wasn't only land, but a great big castle, about ten times the size of our school and a bit more.

So Beryl went and knocked. She was a bit thirsty after all that climbing, and she fancied a bottle of pop.

When the giant saw Beryl standing on his doorstep, he got the most awful shock of his life.

In answer to her knock a big voice bellowed from inside:

"Fee, fi, fo, ferl – I smell the blood of an English girl!"

Then the door opened and the biggest giant you've ever seen – Huh! I bet you've never ever seen ONE giant before! – looked out.

"Hi!" said Beryl. "Or should I say 'High!'"!

The giant peered down at his feet, and there – horror

The giant, it is plain – thinks that Beryl is a pain!

upon horrors – was Beryl peeping up at him.

"F-f-fee, f-f-fi, f-f-fi, f-f-f-ferl – I smell the blood of an English BERYL!" he croaked.

Then he slammed the door in Beryl's face. Or at least, he tried to. For by then Beryl had dodged inside the castle, between the giant's two big boots. As she stood there she amused herself by tying the Big One's bootlaces together. Having done that she popped out and said, "You've got no manners. I only came for a drink of pop. A chap your size must keep his in ten-gallon drums, so I'm sure you can spare a glassful or two."

"G-g-go away, Beryl! I've heard about you!" stuttered the giant, looking very scared. "You're the Peril. That's why I live up h-here in the clouds – to keep away from YOU!"

He turned to run. You can guess what happened. Or if you can't, you should be ashamed of yourself. CRASH!! He fell flat on his face – that's what happened, because, of course, Beryl had tied his laces together.

"Ho! Ho!" laughed Beryl. "Now, come away – untie your bootlaces and lead me to a nice fizzy drink."

"All right," mumbled the giant, rising shakily. "But after you've had it, please go – pup-please!"

He led Beryl to the larder and poured her out the biggest drink she'd ever had in her life – and that's saying something.

"How did you get here anyhow? They haven't started a bus service from the Earth, have they?" asked the giant fearfully.

"Came by the beanstalk," answered Beryl briefly, between two gulps of pop. "You know – you'll have to come down and visit my dad. Otherwise he won't believe me when I say where I've been. He's not scared of me – not like YOU are. But he'd be scared of YOU, and if you were my bodyguard ... see what I mean?"

The giant looked thoughtful and stroked his chin.

"I'll come and protect you from him," he offered, "if you promise not to come visiting up here again. I mean – I'm a big chap, even for a giant. A word from me should keep your Dad in his place for ten years or so."

Beryl hopped into the giant's pocket. She'd just hit on a crafty way of getting a lift

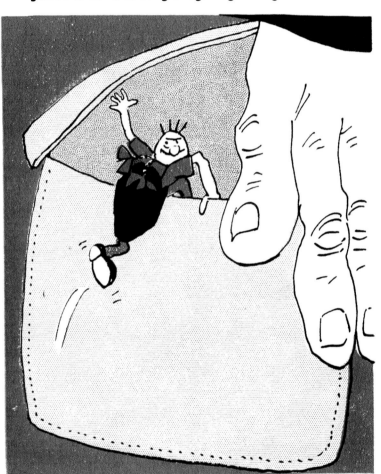

"It's a bargain! Let's go!" whooped Beryl jumping down from the huge table where she'd been standing.

"Aaagh!" yelled the giant in a voice that shook the sky.

"What's up now? Always moaning, you are!" muttered Beryl.

"Ooh! My corn! You landed on my corn!" yowled the giant.

"Serves you right for having such big feet," scoffed Beryl. "Come on, now – to the beanstalk!"

Off she trotted, with the giant hobbling mournfully

There was lemonade by the gallon in the giant's castle – and Beryl was helping to reduce the supplies!

Won't dad be cross –

after her. When they reached the beanstalk Beryl climbed up the giant's legs and hopped into his pocket. She'd just hit on a crafty way of saving herself the trouble of climbing down the beanstalk.

"You can carry me down," she ordered. "The beanstalk mightn't bear the weight of us both at once."

So down the stalk slithered the silly old giant with Beryl comfy and cosy in his pocket. But the Big One was looking very puzzled and seemed to have a problem on his mind.

Near the bottom he nudged his pocket and said to Beryl:

"Here! You know when you said the stalk mightn't bear both of us at once? Well, I've been thinking – even though you're IN my pocket, we're both still on the STALK together, aren't we?"

"If you put it like that – true!" agreed Beryl, grinning. "So I was wrong. The stalk CAN hold us both."

"Er – no!" wheezed the giant. "It's just broken and we're falling straight down. Still, there isn't far to fall – just a hundred thousand feet or so."

"Crumbs!" croaked Beryl. "Quick – have you got a handkerchief?"

"Tch! Tch! Caught a cold, have you? It's the cold air high up that does it," sympathised the giant, handing her a handkerchief the size of a tablecloth.

"Cold, nothing! I'm making this into a parachute," exclaimed Beryl. And so she did, leaping from the pocket when the ground came into sight below through the clouds. "Don't wait for me," she added as the giant crashed on his way, clinging to the broken beanstalk.

BERYL'S BODYGUARD

THE giant's fall ended in Beryl's front garden, right in the middle of the lawn. But he didn't exactly STOP there. The force of his fall made a great twenty-foot hole, in the bottom of which he lay, cross-eyed and groggy.

Beryl parachuted onto the scene a minute or so later. It wasn't a good time to arrive, for Dad came out the house just then to investigate the great THUMP that he'd heard.

The giant crashed down, clinging to the broken beanstalk, while Beryl drifted gently earthwards – by handkerchief!

when he knows he's not the boss!

He stood goggling at the monstrous hole in his lawn. Then he turned slowly to Beryl, who was standing trying to hide the handkerchief parachute behind her back.

"You did it!" he said slowly and scowling furiously. "I don't know how you did it. But you did it!"

"But, Dad," protested Beryl, backing away. "It wasn't – I mean, I didn't do it – "

"IT WAS ME!" From out of the hole appeared the head and shoulders of the giant. "ANY OBJECTIONS?" he demanded in a voice that rattled the window-panes for miles around.

Dad's eyes bulged in his head, and his legs went all wobbly, like jellies.

"Er – no – of course not. I – er, I mean – you're very welcome," he stammered.

"While I'm about it," thundered the giant, "I might as well warn you that you'd better be nice to Beryl. Or you'll have ME to reckon with!"

As he spoke, the giant began to clamber up out of the hole. Poor Dad goggled up at him and turned a sickly shade of green.

"You mean, I can't shout at her, sir?" piped Dad.

"Can't? DAREN'T!" bellowed the giant. Now before I come and - !"

Dad whizzed off at a pace that quite impressed Beryl.

"Gosh, Dad!" she shouted after him. "With a bit of training you might win an Olympic medal. You're GOOD!"

The giant dusted the earth and bits of beanstalk off his clothes and turned to Beryl.

"Well, I've kept my promise," he said. "But now I'm in a pretty pickle. How do I get back home without a beanstalk? That old one's no good!"

"Have you got five shillings?" asked Beryl.

"Just about," admitted the giant. "Why?"

"Well, go down the road to where the old flower-seller sits, and buy a bunch of daffodils. She gives a free magic bean with every bunch. Then you can grow yourself a beanstalk." Beryl laughed again.

"She'll be surprised to see you, I daresay. But if she gives you any trouble just mention MY name. That'll frighten her."

"I can believe THAT," agreed the giant. "I'll be off then. Er – thanks for not playing too many tricks on me."

And the giant marched away with mighty strides.

There's not much more to tell (thank goodness). Beryl never saw the giant again, so he must have got a magic bean and grown himself a beanstalk. Or if he didn't, maybe he's marching around somewhere else, still looking for one. Beryl's pretty sure he'll never come back to see HER, anyway.

Fortunately, Dad doesn't know that.

So Beryl is still living happily ever after ...

The giant boomed out a word of warning to Beryl's Dad – and Dad departed like a rocket!

BANG!
CLANG!
CHRISTMAS TREAT FUND
DRRR!

BUT—
GRR!
CHRISTMAS TREAT FUND
CONFISCATED TO PAY FOR CLASS ROOM DAMAGES
signed Teacher
FUND
CHRISTMAS TREAT
BAH!

HOW CAN WE GET TO THE PANTO?
BE NICE TO TEACHER!
TEACHER'S PET-SIMPERING SIMON SIMPKINS

CER JACK
MAS
WE'LL TAKE THE JOB!
RIP!
BOY WANTED

SO—
MEET MY NEW ASSISTANTS, LADIES.
EEEEK!

LET'S GO, LADIES!
YOU'RE FIRED!

LATER—
LOOK WHAT I FOUND, KIDS!
COO! AN OLD PANTO CAT-SKIN!
HE'S WRONG AGAIN!

PANTO

COME HERE, KIDS!
PANTO

HEE-HEE! OUR PAL'S ONE OF THE UGLY SISTERS!
23-12-67

HERE'S A REALLY HANDSOME AND CLEVER PUPPET FOR YOU TO MAKE OVER THE CHRISTMAS HOLIDAYS, READERS!

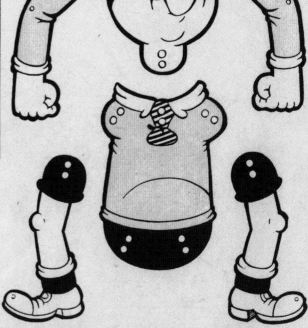

1. STICK PICTURE ON FIRM CARDBOARD.
2. NEATLY CUT OUT PARTS WITH A PAIR OF SCISSORS (CAREFULLY NOW!).
3. BORE HOLES IN PLACES MARKED.
4. LOOP SHORT THREADS THROUGH THE DOUBLE HOLES, AND TIE PARTS TOGETHER (NOT TOO TIGHTLY!).
5. FIT LONG CONTROLLING THREADS TO THE OTHER HOLES IN THE ELBOWS AND TOES—AND WATCH THOSE PUPPETS DANCE AND KICK!

Lots of high jinks with—
MINNIE the MINX
PUPILS WANTED FOR SCHOOL PLAY.
LOOK, MINNIE—ARE YOU GOING TO TAKE PART?
NOT LIKELY—NO SOPPY ACTING FOR ME!
BACK HOME—
I DON'T KNOW, THOUGH—ACTING MIGHT BE FUN IF THEY PUT ON THE RIGHT PLAY FOR ME.
IT MIGHT BE "JULIUS CAESAR"!
TAKE THAT!
HAR! HAR!
OR "RICHARD III"!

A whinny from Minnie!

HO! HO! WE'RE ONLY FOOLING YOU, MINNIE—WE'RE NOT REALLY PUTTING ON "THE SLEEPING BEAUTY"! WE'RE DOING A PLAY I WROTE CALLED "THE FAITHFUL HORSE".

PHEW!

THE NIGHT OF THE PLAY—

HI, READERS! LOOK AT THE PART I'VE GOT! WHINNY!

SO—

AH! HERE IS DOBBIN, MY FAITHFUL HORSE.

MEANWHILE—

COME ON, MINNIE—WE'RE ON!

WAIT A MINUTE—I THINK I'D RATHER BE THE FRONT END OF THIS NAG!

PSSST! WHERE'S DOBBIN?

SO—

COME ON!

DON'T YOU PULL ME ABOUT!

Published 2012 by DC Thomson Annuals Ltd, Courier Buildings, 2 Albert Square, Dundee DD1 9QJ
ISBN 978-1-84535-497-8